THE OFFICIAL STOCKPORT COUNTY QUIZ BOOK

THE OFFICIAL STOCKPORT COUNTY QUIZ BOOK

Best wishes

Compiled by Chris Cowlin
and Kevin Snelgrove

Foreword by Jim Gannon

Best wishes
Chris Cowlin

APEX PUBLISHING LTD

Hardback first published in 2008 by
Apex Publishing Ltd
PO Box 7086, Clacton on Sea, Essex, CO15 5WN, England
www.apexpublishing.co.uk

Copyright © 2008 by Chris Cowlin and Kevin Snelgrove
The authors have asserted their moral rights

British Library Cataloguing-in-Publication Data
A catalogue record for this book
is available from the British Library

ISBN HARDBACK: 1-906358-43-5   978-1-906358-43-3

Typeset in 10.5pt Chianti Bdlt Win95BT

Cover Design: Colin Holland, The Trophy Room Ltd

Printed and bound in Great Britain by
the MPG Books Group

Author's Note:
Please can you contact me: **ChrisCowlin@btconnect.com** if you find any mistakes/errors in this book as I would like to put them right on any future reprints of this book. I would also like to hear from Stockport County fans who have enjoyed the test! For more information on me and my books please look at: **www.ChrisCowlin.com**

This book is an official product of Stockport County Football Club.

We would like to dedicate this book to:

All the players and staff who have worked for the club during their history.

FOREWORD

My affinity with Stockport County began when I arrived at Edgeley Park from Sheffield United. Having come to the professional game relatively late with experience of making a living in the "real world," I quickly related to the Club and its loyal fans. Genuine football fans who had experienced hardship and disappointment, for whom it was a pleasure to strive and deliver success for over the following years. Four Wembley appearances, two promotions and wealth of experience later I was honored with an incredible testimonial celebration. Ten years had passed when I left the club to begin new adventures.

My return as Manager found County five points adrift of safety, facing the reality of losing league status. I felt a mixture of anger and sadness at the demise of the club I love. Driven by deeply felt football principles, I was given the opportunity to work alongside our great backroom staff and excellent young players to share a vision. This shared determination and integrity has delivered the remarkable success of the last couple of years. A level of success the loyal supporters of this Club deserve. Culminating in our victorious win in the Play-Off Final at Wembley Stadium, earning promotion to League One. The pleasure of bringing smiles back to the faces of not only County fans, but to the town of Stockport is difficult to describe. I am truly proud.

I am very pleased to have been asked to introduce this book, which I hope will provide many hours of fun for all County fans and football trivia enthusiasts alike, here's to success in answering the questions and further success on the pitch!

Enjoy the Book
Best wishes

Jim Gannon

INTRODUCTION

I would first of all like to thank Jim Gannon for writing the foreword to this book. Jim is a true legend for County and I am very grateful for his help on this project.

I would also like to thank all the past legends of Stockport County Football Club and many current employees of the club for their comments and reviews on this book (these can be found at the back of the book).

I would also like to thank Peter Wilson, Ian Watts and Des Hicks for their help and advice during the books compilation and Colin Holland for a superb cover design.

I hope you enjoy this book. Hopefully it should bring back some wonderful memories!

It was great working with Kevin Snelgrove for the first time, who is very well organised, between us I hope we have given you a selection of easy, medium and hard questions.

In closing, I would like to thank all my friends and family for encouraging me to complete this book.

Best wishes
Chris Cowlin

Visit Chris Cowlin's website:

www.ChrisCowlin.com

Visit Kevin Snelgrove's website:

www.KevinSnelgrove.co.uk

HISTORY OF THE CLUB

1. Can you name the club's two nicknames?

2. In which year was the club formed - 1881, 1882 or 1883?

3. What is the name of the club's stadium?

4. During the 1933/1934 season, which player scored a record 52 goals for the club?

5. In which year did Stockport County play their first Football League game - 1898, 1899 or 1900?

6. In July 1998, which player became the club's record signing for £800,000 from Nottingham Forest?

7. Which player holds the record for playing the most League games for the club with 489 appearances?

8. In May 1937 the club recorded their record attendance in a League game of 27,304 fans. Which team were Stockport playing - Lincoln City, Leicester City or Manchester City?

9. In which season did Stockport win Division Four - 1956/1957, 1966/1967 or 1976/1977?

10. Who managed the club between 1995 and 1997?

NATIONALITIES

Match up the player with his nationality

11.	Leon McSweeney	English
12.	Gary Dicker	Welsh
13.	Jason Taylor	Australian
14.	Len Allchurch	Republic of Ireland
15.	Conrad Logan	Finnish
16.	Chris Adamson	Finnish
17.	Mark Robertson	English
18.	Chris Marsden	Republic of Ireland
19.	Jarkko Wiss	English
20.	Shefki Kuqi	Republic of Ireland

1990s

21. During the 1990/1991 season, which team did Stockport beat 4-0 at home and 3-0 away in the League?

22. Can you name the four managers that managed the club during the 1990s?

23. On the opening day of the 1994/1995 season, which team did Stockport beat 4-1 at home with Kevin Francis scoring a brace?

24. In February 1999 Stockport beat Birmingham City 1-0 at home in the League, with which striker scoring the only goal?

25. Which striker scored a brace against Ipswich Town at Portman Road during a 2-0 away win in November 1997?

26. Alun Armstrong scored a brace, including a last-minute winner, in a 4-3 win against which team away from home in October 1996?

27. In what position did Stockport finish in the League during the 1995/1996 season?

28. Which two players did Stockport sign from Preston North End in March 1993?

29. Which two strikers finished the 1996/1997 season with 24 League goals between them?

30. Which player finished as top scorer during 1999/2000 with 12 League goals, having played in 44 League matches that season?

SQUAD NUMBERS 2007/2008

Match up the player with his squad number

31.	Chris Adamson	2
32.	Michael Raynes	11
33.	James Smith	6
34.	Adam Griffin	1
35.	Gareth Owen	2
36.	Ashley Williams	3
37.	Robert Clare	32
38.	Liam Dickinson	15
39.	Tommy Rowe	5
40.	Michael Rose	20

WHERE DID THEY COME FROM? - 1

*Match up the player with the team they signed
from to join Stockport County*

41.	Lee Todd	Port Vale (second spell)
42.	Jim Gannon	Macclesfield Town
43.	Chris Marsden	Sheffield Wednesday
44.	Anthony Elding	Notts County
45.	Jim McNulty	Oldham Athletic
46.	Tony Dinning	Hartlepool United
47.	Adam Proudlock	Boston United
48.	David Poole	Sheffield United
49.	Gareth Owen	Yeovil Town
50.	Chris Adamson	Ipswich Town

MANAGERS

*Match up the manager with the year he took over
as manager of Stockport County*

51.	Danny Bergara	1997
52.	Carlton Palmer	1936
53.	Jim Gannon	1989
54.	Andy Kilner	2001
55.	Mike Summerbee	1970
56.	Asa Hartford	1977
57.	Gary Megson	1985
58.	Matt Woods	2006 *(2005 caretaker)*
59.	Bob Kelly	1999
60.	Les Chapman	1987

INTERNATIONALS

*Match up the former County player with the number
of international caps they won for their country*

61.	Asa Hartford	8 England caps, 1 goal
62.	George Best	8 England caps, 2 goals
63.	Carlton Palmer	10 England caps, 2 goals
64.	Mark Robertson	50 Welsh caps 0 goals
65.	Harry Hardy	37 Northern Ireland caps, 9 goals
66.	Jarkko Wiss	50 Scotland caps, 4 goals
67.	Paul Jones	43 Finland caps, 3 goals
68.	Mike Summerbee	18 England caps, 1 goal
69.	Gordon Cowans	1 England cap 0 goals
70.	Frank Worthington	1 Australia cap, 0 goals

LEAGUE APPEARANCES - 1

Match up the player with the number of League appearances he made for the club

71.	Frank Worthington	87
72.	Brett Angell	32 (3)
73.	Harry Hardy	62 (1)
74.	Shefki Kuqi	350 (33)
75.	Paul Jones	151 (5)
76.	Micky Quinn	28 (5)
77.	Jim Gannon	207
78.	Kevin Francis	182 (14)
79.	Danny Boshell	18 (1)
80.	Paul Hart	46

THE LEAGUE CUP

81. Can you name the three goalscorers in the 4-3 2nd round defeat to Charlton Athletic in August 2007?

82. Which team did Stockport beat 1-0 away from home in the 1st round in August 2003, with Stuart Barlow scoring?

83. True or false: Stockport made it to the quarter-finals of the competition during the 2002/2003 season?

84. Which player scored a brace in the 1st round in a 3-0 home win against Carlisle during August 2001?

85. Which team knocked Stockport out of the 2001/2002 competition 8-7 on penalties, having drawn 1-1 in the 2nd round?

86. Can you name the two scorers in the 2-0 home win in the 1st round, 1st leg, during August 1999 against Oldham Athletic?

87. Can you name the two scorers in the 2-1 home win in the 2nd round, 2nd leg, during September 1997 against Birmingham City?

88. Which Lancashire team did Stockport beat 4-1 at home in the 1st round, 2nd leg, during August 1994?

89. Which team did Stockport beat 5-2 away from home in the 2nd round during September 1996?

90. In August 2007 Stockport beat Tranmere Rovers 1-0 in the 1st round of the competition. Can you name the goalscorer?

MANAGERS' WINS

*Match up how many League games the manager won
during his time in charge at the club*

91.	Andy Beattie	31
92.	Jimmy Melia	28
93.	Danny Bergara	63
94.	Jimmy Meadows	1
95.	Dave Jones	21
96.	Eddie Quigley	45
97.	Eric Webster	50
98.	Gary Megson	125
99.	Asa Hartford	45
100.	Brian Doyle	13

POSITIONS IN THE LEAGUE - 1

Match up the season with the position in which Stockport County finished in the League

101.	2007/2008	8th
102.	2005/2006	4th
103.	2003/2004	5th
104.	2001/2002	17th
105.	1999/2000	4th
106.	1997/1998	4th
107.	1995/1996	19th
108.	1993/1994	22nd
109.	1991/1992	9th
110.	1989/1990	24th

ATTENDANCES

Match the attendance record with the Stockport opponents

111.	Record home League 1st May 1937 - 27,304	Hartlepool United
112.	Record home FA Cup 11th February 1950 - 27,883	Manchester United
113.	Record home League Cup 1st November 1972 - 16,535	Hull City
114.	Lowest home League 15th February 1985 - 1,039	Walsall
115.	Lowest home FA Cup 17th November 1984 - 2,781	Tranmere Rovers
116.	Lowest home League Cup 18th August 1987 - 1,476	Southend United
117.	Record away League 30th April 1949 - 38,192	Norwich City
118.	Record away League Cup 30th August 1978 - 42,384	Liverpool
119.	Lowest away League 5th May 1984 - 790	Lincoln City
120.	Lowest away League Cup 2nd September 1986 - 1,433	Carlisle United

PLAY-OFF WINNERS - 2008

121. Who did Jim Gannon recall to the starting line-up in place of Leon McSweeney?

122. What was the Wembley attendance of which 18,000 were Hatters fans?

123. In which positions did Stockport and Rochdale finish in League Two to be eligible for the play-offs?

124. Which team did County beat in the semi-finals over two legs played on 11th May (1-1 draw) and 17th May (1-0 win), aggregate score 2-1?

125. Who scored County's first goal on 33 minutes to equalise?

126. Which player provided the cross for Pilkington to score on 49 minutes with a stooping header?

127. In the match County conceded 7 fouls but how many did Rochdale concede – 9, 13 or 17?

128. Which County player wore a protective mask for a sore cheekbone sustained in the semi-final?

129. Who scored what was to be County's winning goal on 67 minutes?

130. What was the final score when referee Stuart Attwell blew his whistle on 93 minutes?

1999/2000

131. Who was in charge of County during this season?

132. In what position did Stockport finish in the League - 15th, 16th or 17th?

133. Who finished as County's highest League scorer with 12 goals?

134. Following on from the previous question, who was the only other player to score double figures in the League with 10 goals?

135. Against which team did Stockport record their best win of the season, at home in April 2000?

136. True or false: Stockport won on the opening day of the season?

137. Who scored a brace in the 3-3 away draw at Crystal Palace in April 2000?

138. Which East Anglian team beat Stockport 1-0 both home and away?

139. True or false: Stockport didn't win a League game during February 2000?

140. Against which Midlands team did Tony Dinning score in both League meetings, a 3-2 home win and a 2-2 away draw?

WHO AM I? - 1

141. *In 1956 against Accrington Stanley I scored a goal after just seven minutes at the start of the second half. I was born on 24th October 1934 and suffered an attack of meningitis when I was three years old.*

142. *I am a Geordie and signed from Newcastle United in 1994. I made exactly 200 League appearances for The Hatters, scoring 62 League goals. In 1998 I was transferred to Middlesbrough for £1.6m.*

143. *In 10 seasons at Stockport I made 404 League appearances. In December 2004 I left the club after 29 years of service.*

144. *I am Scottish. When I left school I served an engineering apprenticeship. I scored twice in Stockport's biggest ever record home win. Unfortunately a severe ligament injury brought my career to a sudden end.*

145. *I am a blond 6ft 2in striker. My full debut was away at Hartlepool United where I scored twice in a 2-1 win. In an FA Cup tie against non-League Mossley I seriously fractured my leg, which saw me out of the game for 12 months.*

146. *My father owned a decorating business, where I served as an apprentice. I signed for Stockport County on 17th July 1985. I made my final appearance for the club at Wembley in the 1993/1994 play-off final against Burnley.*

147. *I was born in Chester-le-Street, Co. Durham. I am a left-footed player and started my career in 1987 with Huddersfield Town. I retired from football in 1999.*

148. *My career began as a trainee at Aston Villa. I switched to Wolves and helped them move up from the Third Division to the First Division. In June 1995 Dave Jones paid £75,000 for me to join Stockport.*

149. *I was born on 26th June 1970. I was playing semi-professional football with Hallam until 1992, when I signed for County. I remained at the club for nine years, making a total of 361 appearances in League and Cup.*

150. *I was born in 1907. I signed for County in the summer of 1932 and I once scored a hat-trick in three minutes.*

LEAGUE GOALSCORERS - 1

Match up the player with the amount of League goals he scored for the Hatters in his career

151.	Keith Allen	35
152.	Duggie Reid	5
153.	Norman Brown	17
154.	Richard Young	15
155.	Harry Burgess	31
156.	James Stevenson	71
157.	James Smailes	9
158.	Norman Rodgers	23
159.	Les Bradd	72
160.	Frank Clempson	38

THE FA CUP

161. In which season did the club first participate in the FA Cup?

162. Which player scored a brace in the 2-1, 2nd round win in December 2006 at home to Wycombe Wanderers?

163. Which team did County beat 1-0 away in the 3rd round in January 2001, with Karin Fradin scoring?

164. True or false: Stockport once played an FA Cup tie against Shrewsbury Town that lasted 352 minutes?

165. Which team knocked Stockport out of the competition during 1964/1965 and eventually went on to win it?

166. Who scored County's goal in the 1-1 home draw in the 1st round in November 2007?

167. Whom did Stockport beat 2-1 away in the 1st round in November 2006?

168. Following on from the previous question, who scored the goals for Stockport?

169. Which team did Stockport beat 1-0 away from home in the 2nd round during December 1987 - Runcorn, Norwich City or Rotherham?

170. In January 1998 Brett Angell scored twice in a 2-1 away win in the 3rd round against which team?

MATCH THE YEAR - 1

Match up the event with the year it took place

171.	David Logan made his debut for County	1969
172.	Eric Webster left the club as manager	1957
173.	Joseph Hewitt scored the club's first hat-trick in the FA Cup	1961
174.	Tommy Sword was born	1976
175.	Stephen Fleet made his debut for the club	1985
176.	Ray Chapman left the club as manager	1988
177.	Andy Preece scored the club's 5,000th League goal	1975
178.	Jimmy Collier made his County debut aged 16	1893
179.	John Bentley made his debut for the club	1966
180.	Tony Dinning was born	1994

1980s

181. In which League position did County finish during 1985/1986?

182. Stockport's highest home attendance was during 1988/1989, when 6,676 visited to see County play which team?

183. Who managed the club between October 1985 and May 1986?

184. When leaving County, for which club did Chris Marples sign during July 1988 for £28,000?

185. At the end of the 1981/1982 season, County finished in 18th position in League Division Four, level on points with which Yorkshire club?

186. In the 1980s which part of Edgeley Park was filled with concrete and new blue plastic seats fitted?

187. Which end of the ground was demolished following the Bradford fire of 1985?

188. In which League position did County finish during 1983/1984 - 10th, 11th or 12th?

189. In 1986/1987 Andy Thorpe had a spell at which club in between his two spells at County?

190. He scored the winning goal for Norwich City in the 1985 League Cup final and in 1987 became player/coach for Stockport. Who is he?

2000/2001

191. Which team did Stockport beat 3-1 away from home on the opening day of the season?

192. In what position did County finish in the League?

193. How many of their 46 League games did Stockport win - 9, 10 or 11?

194. Who was the club's highest scorer with 12 League goals?

195. Which player signed from FC Jokerit for £300,000 in January 2001?

196. Which player left for Wolves in September 2000 for £700,000?

197. Who was County's manager this season?

198. Which player scored a last-minute winner in the 4-3 home League win against Bolton in October 2000?

199. Which two players both scored a brace in the 4-2 away win at Sheffield Wednesday in December 2000?

200. Which London team did Stockport beat 3-0 during April 2001?

KEVIN FRANCIS

201. In what year was Kevin born - 1967, 1968 or 1969?

202. In what position did Kevin play during his playing days?

203. In what year did Kevin join the club (first spell)?

204. How many League goals did Kevin score during his County career - 77, 88 or 99?

205. Which manager signed Kevin (first spell) and handed him his debut?

206. True or false: Kevin was named the Stockport County Player of the Century?

207. Against which team did Kevin make his County debut as a substitute?

208. For which country did Kevin win full international caps?

209. In what year did Kevin sign for Stockport County (second spell)?

210. When Kevin left County in 1995, which Midlands team did he join?

SAMMY McILROY

211.   In what year was Sammy born - 1950, 1954 or 1958?

212.   What nationality is Sammy?

213.   How many caps did Sammy win for his country, scoring 5 goals - 80, 84 or 88?

214.   In what year did Sammy take over as Stockport manager?

215.   Which team did Sammy manage before Stockport?

216.   In what year did Sammy leave Stockport as manager?

217.   Sammy's first win as County manager came in his third match in charge, in a 1-0 away win against which team?

218.   Sammy took over as manager of which team during May 2006?

219.   Which team did Stockport play during Sammy's first match in charge at home?

220.   Following on from the previous question, what was the score in the match?

DIVISION TWO RUNNERS-UP 1997

221. Can you name the manager who was in charge during this season?

222. Stockport finished two points behind which team?

223. Which two players played in all 46 League games?

224. True or false: Stockport failed to win their first six matches of the League season?

225. Which London team did Stockport beat 5-1 in January 1997, with Andy Mutch, Alun Armstrong, Micky Flynn and Luis Cavaco (2) scoring?

226. Who was County's top scorer with 15 League goals?

227. How many players were used during this League season - 24, 34 or 44?

228. Who scored Stockport's first two goals of the season (in the League Cup) home game against Chesterfield in a 2-1 home win in August 1996?

229. True or false: Stockport were unbeaten in the League in March 1997?

230. How many League goals did Andy Mutch score during the season?

JIM GANNON

231.   Jim was born on 7th August in which year - 1966, 1968 or 1970?

232.   Can you name one of Jim's two nicknames?

233.   In which country did Jim start his senior club football?

234.   In what year did Jim move to Stockport County - 1986, 1988 or 1990?

235.   How many total appearances did Jim make in his County career?

236.   For how many years was Jim a player at the club - 10, 11 or 12?

237.   Jim is ranked number nine in the scoring records for Stockport. How many goals did he score - 64, 67 or 70?

238.   When Jim left Stockport County, for which club did he sign?

239.   True or false: In a career that spanned two decades, Jim holds the unique record of scoring in all competitions, from the then League Division Four to the UEFA Champions League?

240.   True or false: Jim's managerial career started at Shelbourne?

POT LUCK - 1

241. Why was Stockport's game with Bradford at home abandoned in February 1977, losing 2-1 after 71 minutes?

242. What was Stockport's average attendance during 1997/1998 - 7,322, 8,322 or 9,322?

243. Against which team did Stockport play in the Autoglass Trophy final in May 1992?

244. Which goalkeeper captained County to the Third Division Championship in 1936/1937 and then a year later was released from the club?

245. Which two County players were sent off in the Second Division play-off final against Burnley in 1994?

246. Can you name the 17-year-old who made his debut alongside his father in May 1951, a first in the football League, also scoring in the game?

247. Following on from the previous question, whom was the game against?

248. Who was the first Stockport player to win a full international cap for his country?

249. Following on from the previous question, which team did he play against in England's 4-0 win?

250. Which player scored 46 goals during 1933/1934 in the Third Division North?

POT LUCK - 2

251. During 1925/1926 how many goals did County concede in their 42 League games - 37, 67 or 97?

252. Who was manager of County between 1976 and 1977?

253. Who scored the quickest goal in the clubs history, after just 7 seconds against Accrington Stanley on Christmas day 1956?

254. Who was the oldest player, at the age of 40, to appear for County in December 1951?

255. Against which team did County play in Tommy Sword's testimonial match in August 1988?

256. In what position did County finish in the League during 1994/1995?

257. Can you name the only player that played in every League game during 1998/1999?

258. In what year did the club play their first play-off match?

259. Following on from the previous question, against which team did they play in the Fourth Division play-off?

260. Which club knocked Stockport out of the League Cup during 1976/1977 and went on to win the competition?

WHERE DID THEY GO? - 1

*Match the player to the club they joined on
leaving Stockport County*

261. George Best   Retired

262. Kevin Cooper   Chester City

263. Alun Armstrong   Manchester United

264. Billy Johnston   Stevenage Borough

265. Tesfaye Bramble   Bradford City

266. Jermaine Easter   Wimbledon

267. Rickie Lambert   Middlesbrough

268. Mark Bridge-Wilkinson   Wycombe Wanderers

269. Mike Summerbee   Rochdale

270. Trevor Phillips   Cork Celtic

ALAN OGLEY

271.   Where was Alan born - Rotherham, Barnsley or
       Bradford?

272.   True or false: Alan holds the record for the most
       goalkeeping appearances for Stockport?

273.   From which club did Alan join The Hatters -
       Manchester City, Manchester United or Barnsley?

274.   In what year did Alan join County - 1965, 1966 or
       1967?

275.   How many League appearances did Alan make for
       Stockport - 230, 240 or 250?

276.   True or false: the Cheadle End supporters used
       to chant "Here's to you Alan Ogley"?

277.   Yes or no: did Alan ever score in his professional
       football career?

278.   In 1972 Alan played in the League Cup wins over
       which two London clubs?

279.   Alan signed for which club on leaving Stockport -
       Doncaster, York City or Darlington?

280.   In his professional career Alan made how many League
       appearances - 380, 390 or 400?

TREVOR PORTEOUS

281. Where was Trevor born - York, Sheffield or Hull?

282. In what position did Trevor play?

283. Trevor was signed for Stockport County for what fee -
      £1,500, £2,000 or £2,500?

284. In what year did Trevor become player/manager for
      Stockport - 1961, 1963 or 1965?

285. Which team did Trevor sign for in October 1950 where
      he went on to make 61 League appearances and
      scored just the one League goal?

286. True or false: Trevor was manager when Stockport
      won the Fourth Division title in 1967?

287. For how many years did Trevor serve the club - 39, 41
      or 43?

288. True or false: in his time at the club Trevor had a
      variety of roles, including groundsman,
      physiotherapist, scout and youth team manager?

289. True or false: in 1971 Trevor was awarded a
      testimonial on the fifteenth anniversary of his arrival
      at Edgeley Park?

290. Trevor made how many League appearances in his
      professional career - 348, 398 or 408?

JIM FRYATT

291. From which club did Stockport sign Jim?

292. What was Jim's transfer fee to join the club - £7,000, £7,500 or £8,000?

293. What was Jim's trademark for scoring goals?

294. True or false: Jim scored a hat-trick of headers in a 3-1 victory over Bristol Rovers during April 1968?

295. How many League appearances did Jim make for the club - 40, 43 or 46?

296. How many League goals did Jim score while at the club - 29, 31 or 33?

297. True or false: Jim made over 500 League appearances during his career?

298. In 1974 Jim scored his final ever League goal, for which club?

299. With which club did Jim finish his Football League career?

300. In 2002, to celebrate 100 years of football at Edgeley Park, Jim travelled from his home in which US city to be there - Las Vegas, Los Angeles or New York?

ANDY THORPE

301. Where was Andy born - Southport, Stockport or Ellesmere Port?

302. In what year was Andy born - 1960, 1961 or 1962?

303. Andy signed for his final club in September 1997, where he only made two League appearances can you name the club?

304. Andy started playing at right back, but what position did he move to?

305. In between his two spells at Stockport, for which club did Andy play?

306. Between September 1980 and April 1984 Andy played how many consecutive games - 180, 183 or 186?

307. How many League appearances did Andy make for Stockport - 469, 479 or 489?

308. True or false: in all competitions Andy made 555 appearances for The Hatters?

309. After his second spell at Stockport, which other League club did Andy play for?

310. True or false: in 1990 Andy won Stockport Sports Personality of the Year?

2001/2002

311. Against which team did Stockport record their first League win of the season away from home, winning 4-2?

312. Following on from the previous question, can you name both players who scored a brace in the game?

313. Can you name the two players that scored in the 2-1 win against Watford in April 2002?

314. John Hardiker scored two goals in the last five minutes in a 2-1 home win against which club in March 2002?

315. During January 2002, with which club did Stockport draw 3-3 away from home, with Luke Bennett scoring two of the goals and Neil Ross the other?

316. Can you name the three managers that were in charge during this season?

317. When Luke Beckett signed from Chesterfield, how much did County pay for him?

318. In what position did County finish in the League?

319. How many games did Stockport win during the season - 6, 10 or 12?

320. Which player signed from Leicester during November 2001 for £55,000?

SEAN CONNELLY

321. In what position did Sean play for County?

322. How many League goals did Sean score in his County career - 6, 16 or 60?

323. Sean scored two League goals during 1997/1998, against which teams?

324. Which team did Sean sign for in June 2004 and made 42 League appearances during 2004/2005?

325. Which Stockport manager signed Sean for the club and gave him his debut?

326. Against which Lancashire team did Sean make his debut in March 1993?

327. In what year was Sean born in Sheffield - 1969, 1970 or 1971?

328. Which club did Sean join in 2001?

329. Can you name the four managers that Sean played under at Stockport?

330. Against which team did Sean score the only goal in a 1-0 semi-final League Cup (2nd leg) game in March 1997?

BILL ATKINS

331. In 1967 Bill joined Stockport from which club?

332. Against which club did Bill make his Stockport debut?

333. True or false: Bill scored his first goal for County in a 1-1 draw at Crewe Alexandra?

334. In April 1967 Bill scored a 82nd minute headed promotion winning goal against which team?

335. How many League appearances did Bill make for Stockport County - 92, 102 or 112?

336. How many League goals did Bill score with Stockport, a figure matched during his second spell at Halifax Town?

337. After his departure from Stockport, which club did Bill sign for?

338. Following on from the previous question, what was Bill's transfer fee - £16,000, £18,000 or £20,000?

339. With which club did Bill end his League career?

340. True or false: in 2002 Bill was enrolled into the Stockport County Hall of Fame?

HARRY HARDY

341. Harry was born on 14th January in what year - 1890, 1895 or 1900?

342. Where was Harry born - Stockport, Rochdale or Burnley?

343. True or false: to date Harry is the only Stockport player to have played for England?

344. How many times did Harry play for England - 5, 3 or 1?

345. In what position did Harry play?

346. On 4th September 1920 Harry made his debut for Stockport against which club?

347. Harry went on to make how many consecutive appearances - 160, 170 or 180?

348. In the Division Three (North) championship season of 1922 Harry conceded how many goals - 21, 25 or 29?

349. Also in this season Harry played 38 League games, keeping how many clean sheets - 21, 23 or 25?

350. For which club did Harry sign on leaving Stockport?

LEAGUE GOALSCORERS - 2

Match up the player with the highest number of goals scored whilst at the club (in all competitions)

351.	Arnold Jackson	86
352.	Ernie Moss	39
353.	Steve Massey	13
354.	Thomas Meads	48
355.	Ian Helliwell	16
356.	Len Jones	20
357.	Frank Newton	13
358.	Arthur Metcalf	1
359.	John Kerr	21
360.	Andrew Lincoln	7

POSITIONS IN THE LEAGUE - 2

*Match up the season with the position in which
Stockport County finished in the League*

361.	1905/1906	6th
362.	1919/1920	10th
363.	1923/1924	2nd
364.	1992/1993	16th
365.	1993/1994	8th
366.	1996/1997	14th
367.	2002/2003	13th
368.	2003/2004	22nd
369.	2005/2006	19th
370.	2006/2007	4th

BRETT ANGELL

371. In what year was Brett born - 1968, 1970 or 1972?

372. Where was Brett born - Swindon, Marlborough or Cheltenham?

373. On 20th October 1988 Brett first signed for Stockport from which club?

374. From the above question what was Brett's transfer fee?

375. True or false: in 1989/1990 Brett received the Golden Boot for being the Fourth Division top scorer?

376. For which club did Brett sign after his first spell with Stockport?

377. In his two spells at the club, Brett made how many League appearances - 196, 206 or 306?

378. How many League goals did Brett score for Stockport - 78, 88 or 98?

379. Which club did Brett score his first Hatters goal against?

380. True or false: Brett is not enrolled in Stockport's Hall of Fame?

2002/2003

381. Can you name the two players that scored twice in the 4-1 home win in September 2002 against Barnsley?

382. Which team did Stockport beat 3-0 away from home during April 2003 with Aaron Wilbraham scoring twice?

383. Which player scored a hat-trick during a 4-0 home win against Northampton in December 2002?

384. In what position in the League did Stockport finish - 10th, 12th or 14th?

385. How many of their 46 League games did the club win?

386. Luke Beckett was County's top League scorer with how many goals - 23, 25 or 27?

387. Who was County's manager during this season?

388. Which player did County sign from Blackburn Rovers for £400,000 in July 2002?

389. Which striker scored seven League goals in only eight starts and seven sub appearances?

390. Who scored Stockport's goal in the 1-1 draw against Port Vale at home on New Year's Day?

FRANK NEWTON

391. What was Frank's nickname at Stockport County?

392. In what position did Frank play?

393. Which service did Frank represent at football?

394. Which County manager signed Frank?

395. In what year did Frank join Stockport County - 1927, 1928 or 1929?

396. In his first 22 League appearances for Stockport, how many goals did Frank score - 14, 16 or 18?

397. True or false: in September 1929 Frank became only the second Stockport player to score five goals in a match?

398. In 101 League and Cup appearances, how many goals did Frank score - 73, 83 or 93?

399. Which club signed Frank from Stockport County in the summer of 1931?

400. What age was Frank when his football career ended - 32, 34 or 36?

ALF LYTHGOE

401. Alf was born on 16th March in what year - 1905, 1907 or 1909?

402. True or false: Crewe Alexandra released Alf for being too small?

403. In what year did Alf sign for Stockport County - 1926, 1929 or 1932?

404. True or false: Alf scored all five goals in the 5-0 win against Walsall on Boxing Day 1932?

405. How many goals did Alf score in his first season with County - 15, 17 or 19?

406. In his second season with County, Alf scored five hat-tricks in a total of how many League goals - 44, 46 or 48?

407. Which club signed Alf for £3,500 in 1934?

408. During his professional career how many League appearances did Alf make - 184, 192 or 200?

409. How many League goals did Alf score during his professional career - 140, 143 or 146?

410. Which Cheshire League side did Alf manage between 1953 and 1955?

DEBUTS

Match up the player with the club he made his League debut against on the date given for Stockport County

411. Alan Ogley

Walsall,
September 1990

412. Wayne Phillips

Wolves,
March 2000

413. Lee Todd

Mansfield Town,
February 2007

414. John Kerr

Tranmere Rovers,
August 1999

415. Neil Edwards

Tranmere Rovers,
September 1967

416. Dominic Blizzard

Bury,
September 1991

417. Trevor Phillips

Reading,
January 1984

418. John Rutter

Stoke City,
February 1998

419. Martin Taylor

Mansfield Town,
March 1982

420. Laurent D'Jaffo

Newport County,
August 1976

POT LUCK - 3

421. Who scored four goals against Wrexham in February 1957?

422. How many hat-tricks did Joe Smith score in his County career?

423. How many of Danny Bergara's 281 League games in charge did he win - 125, 126 or 127?

424. Which team did County beat 5-0 on the opening day of the 1990/1991 season?

425. Who was the first substitute used in County's history?

426. Following on from the previous question, against which club did he play as substitute away from home in 1965?

427. How many of Dave Jones' 99 League games in charge did he win - 15, 45 or 75?

428. How many goals did County concede in the League during 1921/1922?

429. How much did Kevin Francis cost the club in February 1991?

430. Against which club did Arnold Jackson make his debut in August 1954?

LEAGUE APPEARANCES - 2

Match up the player with the number of League appearances he made for the club

431.	Keith Edwards	2
432.	Peter Fletcher	119 (5)
433.	Charles Robinson	118 (54)
434.	Nigel Smith	115
435.	Mike Summerbee	292 (20)
436.	Aaron Wilbraham	116 (1)
437.	John Price	49
438.	William Raynes	26 (1)
439.	Les Bradd	43 (8)
440.	Keith Allen	86 (1)

2003/2004

441. Can you name the three goalscorers in the 3-0 away win against Chesterfield during April 2004?

442. True or false: Stockport won their first League game of the season on their 13th attempt?

443. In what position did Stockport finish in the League?

444. Can you name the three managers who were in charge during this season?

445. How many of their 46 League games did County win?

446. Which defender signed for County from Aston Villa for £70,000 in December 2003?

447. Who was the top League goalscorer with 12 goals?

448. Who scored the only goal in the 1-0 away win at Brighton during October 2003?

449. How many League goals did Stuart Barlow score during this season, having made 15 starts and 15 sub appearances?

450. Which player left County in August 2003 to join Blackpool on a free transfer?

LEN WHITE

451. Len was born on 23rd March in what year - 1928, 1930 or 1932?

452. Len was born in which English county - Yorkshire, Lancashire or Cumbria?

453. For which League club did Len start his professional football career?

454. Newcastle United signed Len in 1952 for what fee - £8,500, £10,500 or £12,500?

455. From which League club did Stockport sign Len in 1964?

456. True or false: Len scored over 200 League goals in his 16-year career?

457. In what position did Len play?

458. In his career Len only played for four clubs, making how many League appearances - 342, 442 or 552?

459. True or false: Len is still currently Newcastle United's 5th top goal scorer of all time?

460. True or false: in 1958 Len scored a hat-trick in eight minutes, playing for a Football League representative eleven?

HAT-TRICKS

461. Who scored the first Football League hat-trick in the club's history?

462. Who scored a hat-trick against Darlington, away from home, in Division Three in March 1992?

463. Who scored a hat-trick on his last appearance for the club in May 1980 against Halifax Town?

464. Can you name the player who scored a staggering 15 League hat-tricks in his County career?

465. How many hat-tricks were scored by Stockport players during 1995/1996?

466. Which midfielder scored a hat-trick away at Rotherham in February 2008 in a 4-1 win?

467. Who scored a home League hat-trick against Swansea City in a 4-0 win during October 1993?

468. In March 1995, which forward scored a hat-trick in a 5-3 away defeat against Huddersfield Town?

469. In February 1979 Les Bradd scored a League hat-trick against which team?

470. Adam Le Fondre scored four goals in a 5-2 home win against which team in September 2006?

ERIC WEBSTER

471. Which club did Eric sign for in 1952 after serving two years' national service, only making one first team appearance for them?

472. In what year did Eric take over as Stockport manager?

473. How many League games did Eric manage at County - 83, 143 or 203?

474. How many League games did Eric win as Stockport manager - 45, 55 or 65?

475. To which position did Eric guide County in the League during 1983/1984, the highest position during his time as manager of the club?

476. What was Eric's position when he first arrived at the club - groundsman, doctor or Youth team manager?

477. Who took over from Eric as manager of Stockport in 1985?

478. True or false: Eric signed Micky Quinn and gave him his debut in 1982?

479. In what position did Eric finish in the League in his first full season in charge at Stockport?

480. In 1978 Eric was appointed as Stockport's assistant manager, to whom?

MATCH THE YEAR - 2

Match up the event with the year it took place

481.	George McBeth scored the club's 4,000th League goal	1965
482.	John Nibloe was born	1991
483.	Stockport beat Halifax Town 13-0 at home	1962
484.	Chris Beaumont was born	1964
485.	Sean Maloney made his debut and played his only minute of his Stockport career	1977
486.	Arnold Jackson scored the club's 3,000th League goal	1965
487.	Stockport beat Swansea City 5-0 at home on the opening day of the season	1934
488.	Peter Ward was born	1939
489.	Colin Parry made his debut for the club	1979
490.	John Price made his debut for the club	1958

DIVISION FOUR RUNNERS-UP 1991

491. True or false: County were unbeaten during December 1990 in Division Four?

492. Stockport finished one point behind which team?

493. How many games did Stockport win during their 46 League matches?

494. Who was County's manager this season?

495. Whom did Stockport buy in September 1990 from Grimsby Town for £8,500?

496. Which team did Stockport play on the opening day of the season, drawing 0-0?

497. With which Welsh team did Stockport draw 3-3 in September 1990?

498. True or false: Stockport beat Lincoln City 4-0 at home and 4-0 away?

499. Which team did Stockport beat 5-1 at home during January 1991?

500. Which team did Stockport beat 5-0 at home on the last day of the season?

DIVISION TWO PLAY-OFF FINALISTS 1994

501. Who managed County during this season?

502. In what position did Stockport finish in the League?

503. Can you name the two teams who got automatic promotion?

504. Which team did Stockport beat 1-0 on aggregate in the play-off semi-finals?

505. Following on from the previous question, who scored the goal?

506. Which team did Stockport lose to in the final?

507. Following on from the previous question, what was the score?

508. Following on from the previous question, who scored for Stockport in the game?

509. Where was the final played?

510. Can you name the goalscorers for the opponents in the final?

BOBBY MURRAY

511. True or false: Bobby's career began at Inverurie Locos, where he was learning a trade on the railways?

512. What nationality is Bobby - Scottish, Welsh or Irish?

513. True or false: Bobby signed for Stockport County during November 1951?

514. In what position did Bobby play?

515. In how many consecutive League and Cup games did Bobby appear - 224, 226 or 228?

516. Bobby made how many League appearances for County - 445, 455 or 465?

517. Bobby did not miss an FA Cup tie in how many seasons - 9, 11 or 13?

518. True or false: Bobby is 5th in the list of top League appearances for Stockport?

519. How many League and Cup appearances did Bobby make - 490, 495 or 500?

520. On leaving Edgeley Park in May 1963, Bobby went on to work for British Aeorspace, where he spent how many years before retiring - 27, 29 or 31?

DIVISION FOUR CHAMPIONS 1967

521.   How many of their 46 League games did Stockport win - 20, 23 or 26?

522.   How many goals did the team score in the League - 49, 69 or 89?

523.   Can you name the two players who played in every League game?

524.   What was the club's biggest win of the season - 4-0, 6-0 or 8-0?

525.   Following on from the previous question, which team were Stockport playing?

526.   Who was County's top scorer with 11 League goals?

527.   Can you name the manager who led the club to this success?

528.   How many clean sheets did the club record during their 46 League games - 19, 20 or 21?

529.   Who scored the club's only hat-trick during the season, at home to Southend United in a 4-1 home win?

530.   What was the score when County played Lincoln City on the last day of the season - 4-3, 4-4 or 4-5?

POSITIONS IN THE LEAGUE - 3

*Match up the season with the position in which
Stockport County finished in the League*

531.	1928/1929	24th
532.	1936/1937	11th
533.	1947/1948	10th
534.	1951/1952	13th
535.	1953/1954	17th
536.	1955/1956	9th
537.	1967/1968	3rd
538.	1968/1969	1st
539.	1969/1970	7th
540.	1985/1986	2nd

2004/2005

541. How many League games did Stockport win during this season - 6, 16 or 26?

542. Can you name the three managers who were in charge during this season?

543. Which player signed from Bournemouth for £45,000 during July 2004?

544. Who was County's highest League goalscorer with 15 goals?

545. True or false: Stockport failed to win a League game during April 2005?

546. Which centre forward scored seven League goals in 15 appearances during this season?

547. Stockport beat Blackpool 4-0 away during August 2004. Can you name the goalscorers?

548. Which team did Stockport beat 1-0 at home on 26th February 2005?

549. Following on from the previous question, can you name the goalscorer?

550. True or false: Stockport were losing 3-0 away at Barnsley but came back to gain a 3-3 draw during December 2004?

KEVIN COOPER

551. Kevin was born on 8th February in what year - 1971, 1973 or 1975?

552. Kevin was born in which English city - Coventry, Derby or Leicester?

553. In 1997, from which club did Kevin sign, for a transfer fee of £150,000, to go to Stockport?

554. How many years did Kevin spend at the club - 2, 3 or 4?

555. How many League and Cup appearances did Kevin make for The Hatters (both spells) - 167, 177 or 187?

556. Kevin signed for which club for £800,000 in March 2001?

557. True or false: Kevin joined Wolves in 2002 for £1 million?

558. Kevin has played under manager Dave Jones, but how many times - 1, 3 or 5?

559. Kevin only ever played once in the Premiership as a substitute, against whom?

560. With which team did Kevin win a championship medal?

LEAGUE GOALSCORERS - 3

Match up the player with the highest number of goals scored ihe scored in his County career

561.	Percy Downes	41
562.	Colin Parry	12
563.	John Griffiths	19
564.	Joseph O'Kane	0
565.	Michael Davock	6
566.	John Price	27
567.	Charles Danskin	26
568.	Alexander Herd	24
569.	William Moir	31
570.	James Fletcher	35

ASA HARTFORD

571. What is Asa's real first name?

572. In what position did Asa play during his playing days?

573. For which Midlands team did Asa play between 1969 and 1974?

574. In June 2007 Asa was appointed assistant manager at which club?

575. For which country did Asa win international caps, scoring four goals during his career?

576. For which East Anglian team did Asa play between 1985 and 1987?

577. In what year did Asa take over as Stockport manager?

578. Asa's first League win was in his second game in charge of the club, away from home against which team?

579. Who took over as manager when Asa left in April 1989?

580. For which top-flight side did Asa play between 1974 and 1979?

1970s

581. In what League position did County finish during 1970/1971?

582. Who was manager of County between March 1978 and October 1979?

583. Who made his debut against Peterborough United in August 1970 and went on to make 167 (15) appearances for the club?

584. County's highest home attendance during the 1970s was during 1970/1971, when playing against which team?

585. Following on from the previous question, what was the attendance figure - 7,563, 8,563 or 9,563?

586. Can you name the two players who played in every League game during 1972/1973?

587. How much did Manchester City pay for Stuart Lee when he left Stockport in August 1979?

588. Which player scored a hat-trick in the first round of the FA Cup during November 1978 against Morecambe?

589. During December 1979 Stockport paid £25,000 for which player, signing him from Albion Rovers?

590. Which manager was in charge between July 1970 and December 1971, when a total of 65 League games were played?

DANNY BERGARA

591. In what year did Danny take over as Stockport manager?

592. Which manager did Danny take over from at Stockport?

593. For which Spanish club did Danny play between 1967 and 1971?

594. In what position did Danny play during his playing days - defender, midfielder or striker?

595. Which English team did Danny manage before Stockport?

596. What nationality was Danny?

597. In what position in the League did County finish in Danny's first full season in charge of the club?

598. In what year was Danny born - 1938, 1940 or 1942?

599. Which English team did Danny manage during 1996/1997?

600. In what year did Danny leave as manager of County - 1993, 1994 or 1995?

MIKE FLYNN

601. Mike was born on 23rd February in what year - 1967, 1969 or 1971?

602. Where was Mike born - Stockport, Manchester or Oldham?

603. In 1988 Mike signed for Norwich City for £100,000. How many League appearances did he make for them?

604. From which club did Stockport sign Mike?

605. How many League appearances did Mike make for The Hatters - 387, 390 or 393?

606. True or false: Mike received the Supporters' Player of the Year award in the 1993/1994 season?

607. In 1997 which club put a £800,000 bid in for Mike?

608. How many years did Mike play for Stockport - 8, 9 or 10?

609. Which club did Mike sign for on leaving Stockport?

610. Which non-League team did Mike sign for in 2007?

MICKY QUINN

611. Micky was born on 2nd May in what year - 1960, 1962 or 1964?

612. For which club did Micky play as a youth?

613. True or false: Micky made his Stockport debut against Peterborough United, for whom David Seaman was also making his debut?

614. In 1982 Micky moved from Wigan Athletic to Stockport where he eventually made 63 League appearances, scoring how many goals - 35, 37 or 39?

615. True or false: in 2005 Micky was enrolled in Stockport's Hall of Fame?

616. For which club did Micky sign after Stockport?

617. In June 1989 Micky moved to which Premiership club for £680,000, scoring four goals on his debut against the eventual champions Leeds United?

618. In 2003 Micky released his autobiography. What is the title of the book?

619. In 1996 Micky applied for a manager's job, but unfortunately the position went to Adrian Heath - for which club?

620. True or false: Micky appeared on the 2006 series of Celebrity Fit Club, earning the title of Mr Fit Club?

ANDY PREECE

621. Andy was born on 27th March in what year - 1963, 1965 or 1967?

622. Andy was born where - Evesham, Hereford or Worcester?

623. At which club did Andy start his career as a junior?

624. What age was Andy when he made his debut - 16, 17 or 18?

625. True or false: in August 1988 Andy joined Northampton Town, where he made just one appearance as a substitute?

626. From which club did Andy transfer to Stockport?

627. Following on from the previous question, what was Andy's transfer fee - £7,500, £9,000 or £10,000?

628. In the 1993/1994 FA Cup Andy scored the winning goal in a 2-1 giant killing against which club?

629. Andy made 97 League appearances for The Hatters, scoring how many League goals - 40, 42 or 44?

630. Which Lancashire club did Andy manage between 1999 and 2003?

2007/2008

631. In what position did Stockport finish in League Two?

632. Can you name County's manager during this season?

633. Who was County's highest scorer this season, with 19 League goals (excluding play-off matches)?

634. Which player left Stockport and joined Shrewsbury Town in January 2008?

635. True or false: Stockport won their first three League games?

636. Which team did Stockport beat 6-0 at home during December 2007?

637. Following on from the previous question, which player scored a hat-trick in the game?

638. Which player scored the only goal in the 1-0 away win at Lincoln City in March 2008?

639. How many of their 46 League games did the club win?

640. Which player scored a hat-trick in the 4-1 away win in February 2008 against Rotherham United?

LEN ALLCHURCH

641. Len was born on 12th September in what year - 1933, 1935 or 1937?

642. What nationality is Len - Irish, English or Welsh?

643. From which club did Len sign to play for Stockport?

644. In Len's move to County in 1965, what was the transfer fee - £8,000, £10,000 or £12,000?

645. How many League appearances did Len make in his career - 560, 600 or 620?

646. How many League goals did Len score in his career - 108, 112 or 116?

647. How many times did Len play at international level - 9, 11 or 13?

648. How many clubs did Len play for during his 19-year professional career?

649. One of the highlights of Len's career was playing at international level in front of 120,000 fans in the Maracana Stadium, against whom?

650. Len retired from playing at what age - 36, 38 or 40?

JOHNNY PRICE

651. How many League goals did Johnny score in his Stockport career - 14, 24 or 34?

652. How many League appearances did Johnny make for Stockport - 272 (20), 292 (20) or 308 (99)?

653. In what year did Johnny make his County debut?

654. Following on from the previous question, Johnny made his debut against which team?

655. Which County manager gave Johnny his club debut?

656. How much did County pay for Johnny - £400, £4,000 or £40,000?

657. In what position did Johnny play during his playing days?

658. True or false: Johnny was the club's Player of the Year in his first season there?

659. In 1971 Johnny left Stockport to join which club?

660. True or false: Johnny returned to the club for his second spell less than three years after leaving?

WHO AM I? - 2

661. I am Stockport County's record signing, Gary Megson paying Nottingham Forest £800,000 for me.

662. I was born in Mauchline, Scotland, in 1917. I was known as the 'Gentle Giant'. I missed 7 seasons because of World War II.

663. In July 1886 I was the Amateur Athletic Association's 100 yards champion. I was a miner in a Yorkshire Colliery and turned professional footballer in 1889, playing as a goalkeeper.

664. I was only 5ft 3in tall and was a winger, playing on the left. I made my Stockport debut at the start of the 1965/1966 season.

665. I played as a goalkeeper and made 240 League appearances for County until they released me in 1975. The supporters at the Cheadle End used to sing my name to the tune of 'Mrs Robinson'.

666. I was born in Birmingham on 6th December 1967 and am 6ft 7in tall. At a gala dinner to celebrate 100 years of football at Edgeley Park I was named County Player of the Century.

667. I was born just a stone's throw from Edgeley Park. I played as a winger and was paid just £4 a week when I first turned professional. I almost played for England, missing out by just one vote.

668. I was known as the 'Goal Machine', scoring 140 in just 217 appearances for The Hatters. I once scored a hat-trick of hat-tricks in consecutive games. I finished my playing career at Crewe Alexandra.

669. I made my County debut on 13th March 1926 against Hull City. I played as an inside forward and was renowned as a penalty expert.

670. I once featured on the front cover of the *Hotspur Book of Football Stars 1948-49* alongside Blackpool's England international Stan Mortensen. I was born in Halifax in May 1933, and because I was a schoolboy footballer the nickname 'Boy' stuck, making my initials BBB.

67

CLUB HONOURS

Match the club honour with the year

671. Division Two runners-up   *1991*

672. Division Three (North) champions   *1935*

673. Division Three (North) runners-up   *1967*

674. Division Four champions   *1997*

675. Division Four runners-up   *1993*

676. Division Two play-off finalists   *1992*

677. Division Three play-off finalists   *1994*

678. Autoglass Trophy finalists   *1930*

679. Division Three (North) Cup winners   *1970*

680. Cheshire Premier Cup winners   *1922*

JOE BUTLER

681. Joe joined Stockport County in what year - 1896, 1898 or 1900?

682. In what position did Joe play?

683. In June 1905 Joe moved to Clapton Orient after making how many League appearances for Stockport - 75, 100 or 125?

684. Joe moved back to Edgeley Park in what year - 1906, 1907 or 1908?

685. Which club did Joe join for £150 after his second spell at Stockport?

686. Joe played for five clubs during his career - Stockport, Clapton Orient and the club in the previous question, but which other two?

687. How many League appearances did Joe make during his three spells at Stockport?

688. In what year did Joe return for his third Stockport spell - 1916, 1918 or 1920?

689. True or false: Joe was one of the first nominees for Stockport's Hall of Fame in 2002?

690. What was Joe's non-footballing career prior to joining Stockport County?

2005/2006

691. Can you name the two managers in charge of the club this season?

692. In what position in the League did County finish?

693. How many games did Stockport win during their 46 League games - 11, 21 or 31?

694. Who finished as the club's highest scorer with eight League goals?

695. How many goals did Tes Bramble score during this season - 1, 3 or 5?

696. Which two players signed from Oldham Athletic in August 2005?

697. True or false: Stockport failed to win a League game during August 2005?

698. Which team did Stockport beat to record their first League win of the season?

699. Who scored a brace in a 2-1 away win against Chester City during February 2006?

700. Can you name the two goalscorers in the 2-1 League win in March 2006 against Oxford United?

BILL BOCKING

701. Where was Bill born - Blackpool, Southport or Stockport?

702. From which club did Bill join Stockport?

703. In what position did Bill play?

704. True or false: Bill captained Stockport on their record-breaking FA Cup run in 1934/1935?

705. How many League appearances did Bill make for County - 366, 376 or 386?

706. Bill only ever played for two clubs in his professional football career. Can you name the other?

707. True or false: in the summer of 1935, when the main stand on the Hardcastle Road was ravaged by fire, Bill risked his life to rescue his football boots?

708. How many League and Cup matches did Bill play for Stockport - 397, 400 or 403?

709. In his professional career Bill scored how many goals - 6, 12 or 18?

710. At the end of the 1936/1937 season Bill was injured and missed the last how many games - 3, 6 or 9?

LEAGUE APPEARANCES - 3

Match up the player with the number of League appearances he made for the club

711.	Keith Brannigan	23 (1)
712.	Alan Oliver	106 (14)
713.	Neil Bailey	400 (4)
714.	Richard Young	36 (4)
715.	Steven Bullock	18 (3)
716.	John Rutter	139
717.	Matt Woods	8
718.	Vernon Allatt	50 (1)
719.	Keith Webber	85
720.	John Brookes	27

JIMMY STEVENSON

721. What nationality was Jimmy - Irish, English or Scottish?

722. Jimmy signed for South Shields in 1926, which English Division were South Shields in at the time?

723. What was Jimmy's initial trade on leaving school - engineer, miner or painter?

724. True or false: Jimmy was in the record-breaking team that beat Halifax Town 13-0?

725. For how many different League teams did Jimmy play in his career - 4, 5 or 6?

726. How many League appearances in total did Jimmy make - 152, 162 or 172?

727. How many League goals did Jimmy score in his professional career - 54, 64 or 74?

728. Serious ligament problems brought Jimmy's career to a sudden end in what year - 1935, 1937 or 1939?

729. Jimmy had a brief spell managing which club?

730. Jimmy returned to Stockport County in various capacities. How many years did he remain there - 31, 33 or 35?

BILL WILLIAMS

731. In what year did Bill first sign as a professional player - 1979, 1981 or 1983?

732. For which club did Bill first sign as a professional player?

733. In what position did Bill normally play, after playing in midfield?

734. Who recommended Bill to join Stockport County?

735. In October 1988 Bill moved for £50,000 to which club?

736. Following on from the previous question, within two months Bill was transferred back to Edgeley Park for what fee - £20,000, £30,000 or £40,000?

737. True or false: on New Year's Day 1994 Bill was recalled to the first team to help Stockport reach the play-off final?

738. Which player did Bill line up alongside in his final appearance for the club?

739. How many appearances did Bill make for The Hatters - 294, 304 or 314?

740. In which stadium, in May 1994, did Bill make his final Stockport appearance?

WHERE DID THEY COME FROM? - 2

Match up the player with the team they signed from to join Stockport County

741.	Jim McNulty	Leeds United
742.	Dominic Blizzard	Northampton Town
743.	Mark Robinson	Sunderland
744.	Ezekiel Tomlinson	Manchester City
745.	Harpal Singh	Carlisle United
746.	Chris Armstrong	West Bromwich Albion
747.	Peter Clark	Watford
748.	Ali Gibb	Hereford United
749.	Alan Bailey	Macclesfield Town
750.	Brett Angell (2nd spell)	Queen of the South

1960s

751. Which County manager was in charge between 1960 and 1963?

752. Where did Stockport finish in the League during 1968/1969 in Division Three - 3rd, 6th or 9th?

753. Which player made his debut in August 1961 against Colchester United and made a total of 49 appearances, scoring five goals in his club career?

754. Which County manager was in charge between 1966 and 1969?

755. Where did Stockport finish in the League during 1964/1965 in Division Four - 20th, 22nd or 24th?

756. Can you name the only player that played in every League game during 1964/1965?

757. Which County manager, a former goalkeeper, was in charge between 1965 and 1966?

758. Where did Stockport finish in the League during 1961/1962 in Division Four - 12th, 14th or 16th?

759. Where did Stockport finish in the League during 1965/1966 in Division Four - 13th, 15th or 17th?

760. Who scored the club's first League Cup goal in October 1960 against Carlisle United?

JACK CONNOR

761. Jack was born in December of what year - 1919, 1921 or 1923?

762. True or false: Stockport had tried to sign Jack from Rochdale in April 1951?

763. Jack holds the club record for scoring hat-tricks, but how many did he score - 15, 17 or 19?

764. Jack once scored a hat-rick of hat-tricks against which two teams?

765. From which team did Stockport sign Jack in October 1951?

766. What was the transfer fee for Jack's move to Stockport - £2,000, £2,500 or £3,000?

767. How many League appearances did Jack make for The Hatters - 202, 204 or 206?

768. How many League goals did Jack score for The Hatters - 132, 134 or 136?

769. For which club did Jack sign on leaving Stockport in September 1956?

770. How many League appearances did Jack make, scoring 201 League goals in the process - 381, 391 or 401?

WHERE DID THEY GO? - 2

Match the player to the club they joined on leaving Stockport County

771.	Carlton Palmer	Cape Town Spurs
772.	Carlo Nash	Chesterfield
773.	Frank Worthington	Retired
774.	George Purcell	Luton Town
775.	Keith Alexander	Wrexham
776.	George Armstrong	Lincoln City
777.	Gordon Cowans	Manchester City
778.	Andy Dibble	Dublin City
779.	Warren Feeney	Burnley
780.	Glynn Hurst	Swindon Town

FA CUP WINS

Match the result with the season/round

781. 1968/1969 2nd round   **Queens Park Rangers 1**
      Stockport County 3

782. 1987/1988 2nd round   **Stockport County 3**
      Bristol Rovers 2

783. 1934/1935 3rd round replay **Stockport County 5**
      Morecambe 1

784. 1908/1909 1st round   **Runcorn 0**
      Stockport County 1

785. 1924/1925 1st round   **Stockport County 2**
      Barrow 0

786. 2005/2006 2nd round   **Stockport County 5**
      Halifax Town 1

787. 1978/1979 1st round   **Stockport County 3**
      Torquay United 0

788. 1993/1994 2nd round   **Grimsby Town 0**
      Stockport County 2

789. 1964/1965 3rd round replay **Stockport County 1**
      West Ham United 0

790. 1947/1948 3rd round   **Hereford United 0**
      Stockport County 2

2006/2007

791.   In what position did County finish in the League?

792.   How many League games did Stockport win during
        their 46 matches - 21, 23 or 25?

793.   Who was County's manager during this season?

794.   Who signed from Yeovil Town in September 2006?

795.   Which player finished as County's top League scorer,
        scoring 11 goals in only 20 starts?

796.   On the last day of the season, Stockport beat which
        team 5-0 away from home?

797.   How many League goals did Tes Bramble score during
        this season - 6, 8 or 10?

798.   Who was the only player to play in every League game
        this season?

799.   Who left for Torquay United on a free transfer in
        January 2007?

800.   Can you name the three scorers in the 3-0 away win
        against Peterborough United in January 2007?

ANSWERS

HISTORY OF THE CLUB

1. The Hatters or County
2. 1883
3. Edgeley Park
4. Alf Lythgoe
5. 1900
6. Ian Moore
7. Andy Thorpe
8. Lincoln City
9. 1966/1967
10. Dave Jones

NATIONALITIES

11.	Leon McSweeney	Republic of Ireland
12.	Gary Dicker	Republic of Ireland
13.	Jason Taylor	English
14.	Len Allchurch	Welsh
15.	Conrad Logan	Republic of Ireland
16.	Chris Adamson	English
17.	Mark Robertson	Australian
18.	Chris Marsden	English
19.	Jarkko Wiss	Finnish
20.	Shefki Kuqi	Finnish

1990s

21. Lincoln City
22. Danny Bergara (1989-1995), Dave Jones (1995-1997), Gary Megson (1997-1999) and Andy Kilner (1999-2001)
23. Cardiff City
24. Brett Angell
25. Brett Angell
26. Millwall
27. 9th
28. Martin James and Mike Flynn
29. Brett Angell (15) and Alun Armstrong (9)
30. Tony Dinning

SQUAD NUMBERS 2007/2008

31.	Chris Adamson	1
32.	Michael Raynes	15
33.	James Smith	32
34.	Adam Griffin	11
35.	Gareth Owen	5
36.	Ashley Williams	6
37.	Robert Clare	2
38.	Liam Dickinson	20
39.	Tommy Rowe	21
40.	Michael Rose	3

WHERE DID THEY COME FROM? - 1

41.	Lee Todd	Hartlepool United
42.	Jim Gannon	Sheffield United
43.	Chris Marsden	Notts County
44.	Anthony Elding	Boston United
45.	Jim McNulty	Macclesfield Town
46.	Tony Dinning	Port Vale (second spell)
47.	Adam Proudlock	Ipswich Town
48.	David Poole	Yeovil Town
49.	Gareth Owen	Oldham Athletic
50.	Chris Adamson	Sheffield Wednesday

MANAGERS

51.	Danny Bergara	1989
52.	Carlton Palmer	2001
53.	Jim Gannon	2006 (2005 caretaker)
54.	Andy Kilner	1999
55.	Mike Summerbee	1977
56.	Asa Hartford	1987
57.	Gary Megson	1997
58.	Matt Woods	1970
59.	Bob Kelly	1936
60.	Les Chapman	1985

INTERNATIONALS

61.	Asa Hartford	50 Scotland caps, 4 goals

62.	George Best	37 Northern Ireland caps, 9 goals
63.	Carlton Palmer	18 England caps, 1 goal
64.	Mark Robertson	1 Australian cap, 0 goals
65.	Harry Hardy	1 England cap, 0 goals
66.	Jarkko Wiss	43 Finland caps, 3 goals
67.	Paul Jones	50 Welsh caps, 0 goals
68.	Mike Summerbee	8 England caps, 1 goal
69.	Gordon Cowans	10 England caps, 2 goals
70.	Frank Worthington	8 England caps, 2 goals

LEAGUE APPEARANCES - 1

71.	Frank Worthington	18 (1)
72.	Brett Angell	182 (14)
73.	Harry Hardy	207
74.	Shefki Kuqi	32 (3)
75.	Paul Jones	46
76.	Micky Quinn	62 (1)
77.	Jim Gannon	350 (33)
78.	Kevin Francis	151 (5)
79.	Danny Boshell	28 (5)
80.	Paul Hart	87

THE LEAGUE CUP

81.	Adam Proudlock, Anthony Elding, Dominic Blizzard
82.	Lincoln City
83.	False: they were knocked out in the 2nd round by Gillingham
84.	Scott Taylor
85.	Nottingham Forest
86.	Kevin Cooper and Brett Angell
87.	Alun Armstrong and Andy Mutch
88.	Preston North End
89.	Sheffield United
90.	Matty O'Neil

MANAGERS' WINS

91.	Andy Beattie	63
92.	Jimmy Melia	1
93.	Danny Bergara	125

94.	Jimmy Meadows	50
95.	Dave Jones	45
96.	Eddie Quigley	13
97.	Eric Webster	45
98.	Gary Megson	31
99.	Asa Hartford	21
100.	Brian Doyle	28

POSITIONS IN THE LEAGUE - 1

101.	2007/2008	4th
102.	2005/2006	22nd
103.	2003/2004	19th
104.	2001/2002	24th
105.	1999/2000	17th
106.	1997/1998	8th
107.	1995/1996	9th
108.	1993/1994	4th
109.	1991/1992	5th
110.	1989/1990	4th

RECORD ATTENDANCES

111.	Record home League		
	1st May 1937 - 27,304	Lincoln City	
112.	Record home FA Cup		
	11th February 1950 - 27,883	Liverpool	
113.	Record home League Cup		
	1st November 1972 - 16,535	Norwich City	
114.	Lowest home League		
	15th February 1985 - 1,039	Southend United	
115.	Lowest home FA Cup		
	17th November 1984 - 2,781	Walsall	
116.	Lowest home League Cup		
	18th August 1987 - 1,476	Carlisle United	
117.	Record away League		
	30th April 1949 - 38,192	Hull City	
118.	Record away League Cup		
	30th August 1978 - 42,384	Manchester United	

119.	Lowest away League	
	5th May 1984 - 790	Hartlepool United
120.	Lowest away League Cup	
	2nd September 1986 - 1,433	Tranmere Rovers

PLAY-OFF WINNERS - 2008

121.	Anthony Pilkington
122.	35,715
123.	Stockport County: 4th with 82 points
	Rochdale: 5th with 80 points
124.	Wycombe Wanderers
125.	Own goal by Rochdale player Nathan Stanton
126.	Michael Rose
127.	17
128.	Gareth Owen
129.	Liam Dickinson
130.	Stockport County 3, Rochdale 2

1999/2000

131.	Andy Kilner
132.	17th
133.	Tony Dinning
134.	Ian Moore
135.	Swindon Town
136.	True: 1-0 against Grimsby Town
137.	Ian Moore
138.	Ipswich Town
139.	True: lost 2 and drew 2
140.	Wolves

WHO AM I? - 1

141.	Ray Drake
142.	Alun Armstrong
143.	John Rutter
144.	Jimmy Stevenson
145.	Tommy Sword
146.	Bill Williams
147.	Peter Ward

148.	Tom Bennett

149.	Sean Connelly

150.	Alf Lythgoe

LEAGUE GOALSCORERS - 1

151.	Keith Allen	15
152.	Duggie Reid	23
153.	Norman Brown	9
154.	Richard Young	5
155.	Harry Burgess	71
156.	James Stevenson	38
157.	James Smailes	17
158.	Norman Rodgers	72
159.	Les Bradd	31
160.	Frank Clempson	35

THE FA CUP

161.	1892/1893

162.	Adam Proudlock

163.	Preston North End

164.	True: In December 1947

165.	Liverpool

166.	Matty McNeil

167.	Exeter City

168.	Tes Bramble and Adam Proudlock

169.	Runcorn

170.	Preston North End

MATCH THE YEAR - 1

171.	David Logan made his debut for County	1988
172.	Eric Webster left the club as manager	1985
173.	Joseph Hewitt scored the club's first hat-trick in the FA Cup	1893
174.	Tommy Sword was born	1957
175.	Stephen Fleet made his debut for the club	1966
176.	Ray Chapman left the club as manager	1976
177.	Andy Preece scored the club's 5,000th League goal	1994
178.	Jimmy Collier made his County debut aged 16	1969

| 179. | John Bentley made his debut for the club | 1961 |
| 180. | Tony Dinning was born | 1975 |

1980s

181.	11th
182.	Burnley
183.	Les Chapman
184.	York City
185.	Halifax Town
186.	The Paddock (in front of the Main Stand)
187.	The Cheadle End
188.	12th
189.	Tranmere Rovers
190.	Asa Hartford

2000/2001

191.	Gillingham
192.	19th
193.	11
194.	Aaron Wilbraham
195.	Shefki Kuqi
196.	Tony Dinning
197.	Andy Kilner
198.	Aaron Wilbraham
199.	Kevin Cooper and Karim Fradin
200.	Queens Park Rangers

KEVIN FRANCIS

201.	1967
202.	Striker
203.	1991
204.	88
205.	Danny Bergara
206.	True
207.	Lincoln City
208.	Saint Kitts and Nevis
209.	2000
210.	Birmingham City

SAMMY McILROY

211. 1954
212. Northern Irish
213. 88
214. 2003
215. Northern Ireland
216. 2004
217. Brighton & Hove Albion, October 2003
218. Morecambe
219. Notts County
220. 2-2

DIVISION TWO RUNNERS-UP 1997

221. Dave Jones
222. Bury
223. Micky Flynn and Paul Jones
224. True
225. Millwall
226. Brett Angell
227. 24
228. Andy Mutch
229. True
230. 5

JIM GANNON

231. 1968
232. 'Jimbo' or 'The Ghost'
233. Ireland
234. 1990
235. 480
236. 10 (9 March 1990 to 21 March 2000)
237. 64
238. Crewe Alexandra
239. True
240. False: it started at Dundalk

POT LUCK - 1

241. Waterlogged pitch

242. 8,322
243. Stoke City
244. Frank McDonough
245. Mike Wallace and Chris Beaumont
246. David Herd
247. Hartlepools United
248. Harry Hardy
249. Belgium
250. Alf Lythgoe

POT LUCK - 2

251. 97
252. Eddie Quigley
253. Ray Drake
254. Alec Herd
255. Manchester City
256. 11th
257. Mike Flynn
258. 1990
259. Chesterfield
260. Everton

WHERE DID THEY GO? - 1

261. George Best   Cork Celtic
262. Kevin Cooper   Wimbledon
263. Alun Armstrong   Middlesbrough
264. Billy Johnston   Manchester United
265. Tesfaye Bramble   Stevenage Borough
266. Jermaine Easter   Wycombe Wanderers
267. Rickie Lambert   Rochdale
268. Mark Bridge-Wilkinson Bradford City
269. Mike Summerbee   Retired
270. Trevor Phillips   Chester City

ALAN OGLEY

271. Barnsley
272. False: second to Tiger Bowles
273. Manchester City

274. *1967*

275. *240*

276. *True*

277. *No*

278. *Crystal Palace and West Ham*

279. *Darlington*

280. *380*

TREVOR PORTEOUS

281. *Hull*

282. *Defender*

283. *£1,500*

284. *1963*

285. *Hull City*

286. *False: he was assistant manager*

287. *41*

288. *True*

289. *False: his testimonial was in 1966 on the tenth anniversary*

290. *398*

JIM FRYATT

291. *Torquay United*

292. *£7,500*

293. *Bullet header*

294. *True*

295. *46*

296. *29*

297. *False: he made 499 League appearances*

298. *Stockport County*

299. *Torquay United*

300. *Las Vegas*

ANDY THORPE

301. *Stockport*

302. *1960*

303. *Doncaster Rovers*

304. *Central defender*

305. *Tranmere Rovers*

306. 183
307. 489
308. True
309. Doncaster Rovers
310. True

2001/2002

311. Bradford City
312. Glynn Hurst and Scott Taylor
313. Fraser McLachlan and Luke Beckett
314. Manchester City
315. Gillingham
316. Andy Kilner, Craig Madden and Carlton Palmer
317. £100,000
318. 24th
319. 6
320. Kevin Ellison

SEAN CONNELLY

321. Defender
322. 6
323. Middlesbrough (home) and Birmingham City (away)
324. Rushden & Diamonds
325. Danny Bergara
326. Preston North End
327. 1970
328. Wolves
329. Danny Bergara, Dave Jones, Gary Megson and Andy Kilner
330. Middlesbrough

BILL ATKINS

331. Halifax Town
332. Halifax Town
333. True
334. Notts County
335. 92
336. 37
337. Portsmouth

338.	£18,000
339.	Darlington
340.	True

HARRY HARDY

341.	1895
342.	Stockport
343.	True
344.	1
345.	Goalkeeper
346.	Cardiff City
347.	170
348.	21
349.	23
350.	Everton

LEAGUE GOALSCORERS - 2

351.	Arnold Jackson	48
352.	Ernie Moss	7
353.	Steve Massey	20
354.	Thomas Meads	21
355.	Ian Helliwell	13
356.	Len Jones	1
357.	Frank Newton	86
358.	Arthur Metcalf	13
359.	John Kerr	16
360.	Andrew Lincoln	39

POSITIONS IN THE LEAGUE - 2

361.	1905/1906	10th
362.	1919/1920	16th
363.	1923/1924	13th
364.	1992/1993	6th
365.	1993/1994	4th
366.	1996/1997	2nd
367.	2002/2003	14th
368.	2003/2004	19th
369.	2005/2006	22nd

370.	2006/2007	8th

BRETT ANGELL

371.	1968
372.	Marlborough
373.	Derby County
374.	£33,000 a then County record
375.	True
376.	Southend United
377.	196
378.	78
379.	Hartlepool United
380.	False: he was enrolled on 12th October 2002

2002/2003

381.	Jim Goodwin and Luke Beckett
382.	Northampton Town
383.	Luke Beckett
384.	14th
385.	15
386.	27
387.	Carlton Palmer
388.	Ben Burgess
389.	Aaron Wilbraham
390.	Ben Burgess

FRANK NEWTON

391.	Bonzo
392.	Centre forward
393.	RAF
394.	Lincoln Hyde
395.	1928 (13th January)
396.	18
397.	True (Alf Lythgoe was the first)
398.	93
399.	Fulham
400.	32

ALF LYTHGOE

401.	*1907*
402.	*True*
403.	*1932*
404.	*False: he scored two of the goals*
405.	*19*
406.	*46*
407.	*Huddersfield Town*
408.	*192*
409.	*146*
410.	*Altrincham*

DEBUTS

411.	*Alan Ogley*	*Tranmere Rovers, September 1967*
412.	*Wayne Phillips*	*Stoke City, February 1998*
413.	*Lee Todd*	*Walsall, September 1990*
414.	*John Kerr*	*Reading, January 1984*
415.	*Neil Edwards*	*Bury, September 1991*
416.	*Dominic Blizzard*	*Mansfield Town, February 2007*
417.	*Trevor Phillips*	*Mansfield Town, March 1982*
418.	*John Rutter*	*Newport County, August 1976*
419.	*Martin Taylor*	*Wolves, March 2000*
420.	*Laurent D'Jaffo*	*Tranmere Rovers, August 1999*

POT LUCK - 3

421.	*Ray Drake*
422.	*8*
423.	*125*
424.	*Swansea City*
425.	*Frank Beaumont*
426.	*Chester*
427.	*45*
428.	*21*
429.	*£60,000*
430.	*Carlisle United*

LEAGUE APPEARANCES - 2

431.	*Keith Edwards*	*26 (1)*

432.	Peter Fletcher	43 (8)
433.	Charles Robinson	115
434.	Nigel Smith	119 (5)
435.	Mike Summerbee	86 (1)
436.	Aaron Wilbraham	118 (54)
437.	John Price	292 (20)
438.	William Raynes	2
439.	Les Bradd	116 (1)
440.	Keith Allen	49

2003/2004

441. Rickie Lambert, Jon Daly and Danny Jackman
442. False: Stockport beat Peterborough United on 30 August 2003
443. 19th
444. Carlton Palmer, John Hollins and Sammy McIlroy
445. 11
446. Danny Jackman
447. Rickie Lambert
448. Aaron Wilbraham
449. 8
450. Lee Jones

LEN WHITE

451. 1930
452. Yorkshire
453. Rotherham
454. £12,500
455. Huddersfield Town
456. True: he scored 218
457. Winger/forward
458. 442
459. False: he's 3rd with 153 goals
460. True

HAT-TRICKS

461. Joe Foster
462. Andy Preece
463. Eddie Prudham

464.	Jack Connor
465.	2: Andy Mutch (against Oxford United, League) and Jeff Eckhardt (against Lincoln City, FA Cup)
466.	Tommy Rowe
467.	Andy Preece
468.	Warren Feeney
469.	Barnsley
470.	Wrexham

ERIC WEBSTER

471.	Manchester City
472.	1982
473.	143
474.	45
475.	12th
476.	Youth team manager
477.	Colin Murphy
478.	True
479.	16th
480.	Mike Summerbee

MATCH THE YEAR - 2

481.	George McBeth scored the club's 4,000th League goal	1977
482.	John Nibloe was born	1939
483.	Stockport beat Halifax Town 13-0 at home	1934
484.	Chris Beaumont was born	1965
485.	Sean Maloney made his debut and played his only minute of his Stockport career	1979
486.	Arnold Jackson scored the club's 3,000th League goal	1958
487.	Stockport beat Swansea City 5-0 at home on the opening day of the season	1991
488.	Peter Ward was born	1964
489.	Colin Parry made his debut for the club	1962
490.	John Price made his debut for the club	1965

DIVISION FOUR RUNNERS-UP 1991

491. *True: 2 wins and 3 draws*
492. *Darlington*
493. *23*
494. *Danny Bergara*
495. *Keith Alexander*
496. *Halifax Town*
497. *Cardiff City*
498. *False: Stockport beat Lincoln City 4-0 at home and 3-0 away*
499. *Halifax Town*
500. *Scunthorpe United*

DIVISION TWO PLAY-OFF FINALISTS 1994

501. *Danny Bergara*
502. *4th*
503. *Reading and Port Vale*
504. *York City*
505. *Chris Beaumont*
506. *Burnley*
507. *2-1 to Burnley*
508. *Chris Beaumont*
509. *Wembley*
510. *David Eyres and Gary Parkinson*

BOBBY MURRAY

511. *True*
512. *Scottish*
513. *True*
514. *Halfback*
515. *226*
516. *465*
517. *11*
518. *False: he's 2nd*
519. *495*
520. *27*

DIVISION FOUR CHAMPIONS 1967

521. *26*

522. 69

523. Billy Haydock and Matt Woods

524. 4-0 (goals by John Price, Frank Lord [2] and Norman Sykes)

525. Bradford (Park Avenue)

526. Bert Lister

527. Jimmy Meadows

528. 19

529. Bert Lister

530. 4-5

POSITIONS IN LEAGUE - 3

531.	1928/1929	2nd
532.	1936/1937	1st
533.	1947/1948	17th
534.	1951/1952	3rd
535.	1953/1954	10th
536.	1955/1956	7th
537.	1967/1968	13th
538.	1968/1969	9th
539.	1969/1970	24th
540.	1985/1986	11th

2004/2005

541. 6

542. Sammy McIlroy, Mark Lillis and Chris Turner

543. Warren Feeney

544. Warren Feeney

545. True: 1 draw and 5 defeats

546. Luke Beckett

547. Danny Jackman, Warren Feeney and Luke Beckett (2)

548. Hartlepool United

549. Warren Feeney

550. True

KEVIN COOPER

551. 1975

552. Derby

553. Derby County

554. 4
555. 187
556. Wimbledon
557. True
558. 3
559. Charlton Athletic
560. Norwich City

LEAGUE GOALSCORERS - 3

561.	Percy Downes	27
562.	Colin Parry	0
563.	John Griffiths	31
564.	Joseph O'Kane	12
565.	Michael Davock	41
566.	John Price	24
567.	Charles Danskin	6
568.	Alexander Herd	35
569.	William Moir	26
570.	James Fletcher	19

ASA HARTFORD

571. Richard
572. Midfielder
573. West Bromwich Albion
574. Macclesfield Town
575. Scotland
576. Norwich City
577. 1987
578. Darlington
579. Danny Bergara
580. Manchester City

1970s

581. 11th
582. Mike Summerbee
583. John Griffiths
584. Oldham Athletic
585. 9,563

586. *Alan Ogley and Tommy Spratt*
587. *£80,000*
588. *Terry Park*
589. *Tony Coyle*
590. *Matt Woods*

DANNY BERGARA
591. *1989*
592. *Asa Hartford*
593. *Sevilla*
594. *Striker*
595. *Rochdale*
596. *Uruguayan*
597. *4th*
598. *1942*
599. *Rotherham United*
600. *1995*

MIKE FLYNN
601. *1969*
602. *Oldham*
603. *None*
604. *Preston North End*
605. *387*
606. *True*
607. *Birmingham City*
608. *9*
609. *Barnsley*
610. *Radcliffe Borough*

MICKY QUINN
611. *1962*
612. *Derby County*
613. *True*
614. *39*
615. *True*
616. *Oldham Athletic*
617. *Newcastle United*

618. *Who Ate All The Pies?*

619. Burnley

620. True

ANDY PREECE

621. 1967

622. Evesham

623. Worcester City

624. 16

625. True

626. Wrexham

627. £10,000

628. Queens Park Rangers

629. 42

630. Bury

2007/2008

631. 4th

632. Jim Gannon

633. Liam Dickinson

634. Keith Briggs

635. False: 1 win and 2 draws

636. Wycombe Wanderers

637. Adam Proudlock

638. David Poole

639. 24

640. Tommy Rowe

LEN ALLCHURCH

641. 1933

642. Welsh

643. Sheffield United

644. £10,000

645. 600

646. 108

647. 11

648. 3

649. Brazil

650.   38

JOHNNY PRICE
651.   24
652.   292 (20)
653.   1965
654.   Chester City
655.   Trevor Porteous
656.   £4,000
657.   Winger
658.   True
659.   Blackburn Rovers
660.   True

WHO AM I? - 2
661.   Ian Moore
662.   Duggie Reid
663.   Arthur Wharton
664.   Johnny Price
665.   Alan Ogley
666.   Kevin Francis
667.   Ted Critchley
668.   Jack Connor
669.   Harry Burgess
670.   Bryan 'Boy' Brennan

CLUB HONOURS

671.	Division Two runners-up	1997
672.	Division Three (North) champions	1922
673.	Division Three (North) runners-up	1930
674.	Division Four champions	1967
675.	Division Four runners-up	1991
676.	Division Two play-off finalists	1994
677.	Division Three play-off finalists	1992
678.	Autoglass Trophy finalists	1993
679.	Division Three (North) Cup winners	1935
680.	Cheshire Premier Cup winners	1970

JOE BUTLER

681. 1898
682. Goalkeeper
683. 100
684. 1906
685. Glossop
686. Sunderland and Lincoln City
687. 174
688. 1916
689. True
690. Miner

2005/2006

691. Chris Turner and Jim Gannon
692. 22nd
693. 11
694. Jermaine Easter
695. 5
696. Danny Boshall and Dean Crowe
697. True
698. Grimsby Town, 3-1 away win in September 2005
699. Liam Dickinson
700. Tes Bramble and Adam La Fondre

BILL BOCKING

701. Stockport
702. Hyde United
703. Fullback
704. True
705. 366
706. Everton
707. True
708. 397
709. 6
710. 9

LEAGUE APPEARANCES - 3

711.	Keith Brannigan	8
712.	Alan Oliver	139
713.	Neil Bailey	50 (1)
714.	Richard Young	27
715.	Steven Bullock	106 (14)
716.	John Rutter	400 (4)
717.	Matt Woods	85
718.	Vernon Allatt	23 (1)
719.	Keith Webber	36 (4)
720.	John Brookes	18 (3)

JIMMY STEVENSON

721. Scottish
722. English Second Division
723. Engineer
724. True
725. 4 (South Shields, Bradford C, County and Walsall)
726. 172
727. 64
728. 1935
729. Macclesfield Town
730. 35 years

BILL WILLIAMS

731. 1981
732. Rochdale
733. Central defender
734. Les Chapman
735. Manchester City
736. £30,000
737. True
738. Mike Flynn
739. 314
740. Wembley

WHERE DID THEY COME FROM? - 2

741. Jim McNulty   Macclesfield Town

742.	Dominic Blizzard	Watford
743.	Mark Robinson	Hereford United
744.	Ezekiel Tomlinson	West Bromwich Albion
745.	Harpal Singh	Leeds United
746.	Chris Armstrong	Queen of the South
747.	Peter Clark	Carlisle United
748.	Ali Gibb	Northampton Town
749.	Alan Bailey	Manchester City
750.	Brett Angell	Sunderland

1960s

751.	Reg Flewin
752.	9th
753.	John Bentley
754.	Jimmy Meadows
755.	24th
756.	Colin Parry
757.	Bert Trautmann
758.	16th
759.	13th
760.	Gene Wilson

JACK CONNOR

761.	1919
762.	True
763.	17
764.	Chester City (twice) and Crewe Alexandra
765.	Bradford City
766.	£2,500
767.	206
768.	132
769.	Crewe Alexandra
770.	381

WHERE DID THEY GO? - 2

771.	Carlton Palmer	Dublin City
772.	Carlo Nash	Manchester City
773.	Frank Worthington	Cape Town Spurs

774.	George Purcell	Swindon Town
775.	Keith Alexander	Lincoln City
776.	George Armstrong	Retired
777.	Gordon Cowans	Burnley
778.	Andy Dibble	Wrexham
779.	Warren Feeney	Luton Town
780.	Glynn Hurst	Chesterfield

FA CUP WINS

781.	1968/1969 2nd round	Stockport County 2 Barrow 0
782.	1987/1988 2nd round	Runcorn 0 Stockport County 1
783.	1934/1935 3rd round replay	Stockport County 1 West Ham United 0
784.	1908/1909 1st round	Grimsby Town 0 Stockport County 2
785.	1924/1925 1st round	Queens Park Rangers 1 Stockport County 3
786.	2005/2006 2nd round	Hereford United 0 Stockport County 2
787.	1978/1979 1st round	Stockport County 5 Morecambe 1
788.	1993/1994 2nd round	Stockport County 5 Halifax Town 1
789.	1964/1965 3rd round replay	Stockport County 3 Bristol Rovers 2
790.	1947/1948 3rd round	Stockport County 3 Torquay United 0

2006/2007

791.	8th
792.	21
793.	Jim Gannon
794.	David Poole
795.	Anthony Elding
796.	Darlington
797.	6

NOTES

NOTES

NOTES

NOTES

NOTES

NOTES

NOTES